Chopin
2010

WYDANIE NARODOWE
DZIEŁ FRYDERYKA CHOPINA

NATIONAL EDITION
OF THE WORKS OF FRYDERYK CHOPIN

VARIATIONS Op. 2
ON "LA CI DAREM LA MANO"
FROM "DON GIOVANNI"
FOR PIANO AND ORCHESTRA
Score

NATIONAL EDITION
Edited by JAN EKIER

Foundation
for the National Edition
of the Works of Fryderyk Chopin

PWM
EDITION

SERIES A. WORKS PUBLISHED DURING CHOPIN'S LIFETIME. VOLUME XVa

FRYDERYK CHOPIN

WARIACJE Op. 2
NA TEMAT
Z „DON GIOVANNIEGO" MOZARTA
NA FORTEPIAN I ORKIESTRĘ
Partytura

WYDANIE NARODOWE
Redaktor naczelny: JAN EKIER

FUNDACJA WYDANIA NARODOWEGO
POLSKIE WYDAWNICTWO MUZYCZNE SA
WARSZAWA 2020

SERIA A. UTWORY WYDANE ZA ŻYCIA CHOPINA. TOM XVa

Redakcja tomu: Jan Ekier, Paweł Kamiński

Komentarz wykonawczy i Komentarz źródłowy (skrócony) dołączone są do nut głównej
serii *Wydania Narodowego* oraz do strony internetowej www.chopin-nationaledition.com

Pełne *Komentarze źródłowe* do poszczególnych tomów będą publikowane oddzielnie.

Wydany w oddzielnym tomie *Wstęp do Wydania Narodowego Dzieł Fryderyka Chopina*
– 1. Zagadnienia edytorskie obejmuje całokształt ogólnych problemów wydawniczych,
zaś *Wstęp... – 2. Zagadnienia wykonawcze* – całokształt ogólnych problemów interpretacyjnych.
Pierwsza część *Wstępu* jest także dostępna na stronie www.pwm.com.pl

Wariacje w autentycznym układzie na jeden fortepian znajdują się w tomie *Utwory koncertowe* 15 **A XIVa**,
a wersja z wyciągiem fortepianowym w tomie *Utwory koncertowe* 32 **B VII**.

Głosy orkiestrowe dostępne do wypożyczenia w Bibliotece Materiałów Orkiestrowych PWM,
ul. Fredry 8, 00-097 Warszawa, tel. 22 635-35-50 / fax 22 826-97-80
www.pwm.com.pl / e-mail: bmo@pwm.com.pl

Editors of this Volume: Jan Ekier, Paweł Kamiński

A *Performance Commentary* and a *Source Commentary (abridged)* are included in the
music of the main series of the *National Edition* and available on www.chopin-nationaledition.com

Full *Source Commentaries* on each volume will be published separately.

The *Introduction to the National Edition of the Works of Fryderyk Chopin*
1. Editorial Problems, published as a separate volume, covers general matters concerning the publication.
The *Introduction... 2. Problems of Performance* covers all general questions of the interpretation.
First part of the *Introduction* is also available on the website www.pwm.com.pl

Variations in authentic arrangement for one piano are to be found in the volume *Concert Works* 15 **A XIVa**,
and the version with the piano arrangement in the volume *Concert Works* 32 **B VII**.

Orchestral parts can be borrowed from the Library of Orchestral Materials of the PWM Edition,
Fredry 8, 00-097 Warszawa, tel. + 48 22 635-35-50 / fax + 48 22 826-97-80
www.pwm.com.pl / e-mail: bmo@pwm.com.pl

Wariacje B-dur op. 2 / Variations in B♭ major Op. 2

THEMA

INTRODUZIONE

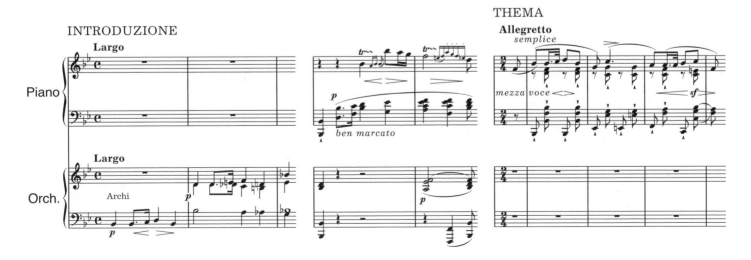

about the Variations…

Op. 2

'[…] I've the following request. Since the weather is foul, I would gladly write out a fair copy of the piano part for the Variations. For that I need your copy, so I would be grateful if you could bring it to me tomorrow, and the day after you'll receive both one and the other.'

From a letter sent by Chopin to Jan Matuszyński in Warsaw, Warsaw winter 1827/1828.

'I think the Trio will meet a similar fate to my Sonata and Variations. They are already in Leipzig, the former, as you know, dedicated to Elsner; on the latter (perhaps too boldly) I inscribed your name. (Thus bade my heart, friendship did not forbid, and you – think not badly of it.)'

From a letter sent by Chopin to Tytus Woyciechowski in Poturzyn, Warsaw 9 September 1828.

'[…] and so yesterday, that is Tuesday, at 7 in the evening, at the imperial-royal opera house, I presented myself to the world! [...] As soon as I took to the stage, I received an ovation; after playing each variation the applause was so great I couldn't hear the orchestra's tutti. When I finished, the clapping was such that I had to come out and bow again.'

From a letter sent by Chopin to his family in Warsaw, Vienna 12 August 1829.

'In the second concert I also had to play the Variations again, as they were terribly popular with the ladies and Haslinger. They are to be published in the Odeon; quite an honour, I should think.'

From a letter sent by Chopin to Tytus Woyciechowski in Poturzyn, Warsaw 12 September 1829.

'Miss Belleville played my printed Vari[ations] in Vienna, and she even knows one by heart.'

From a letter sent by Chopin to Tytus Woyciechowski in Poturzyn, Warsaw 5 June 1830.

'Also yesterday I went with Kandler to the imperial library. […] imagine my surprise when among the newer manuscripts I see a book in a case with the inscription Chopin. It's quite thick, in an attractive binding. I think to myself, I've never heard of any other Chopin […] Kandler takes it out; I take a look, my hand—Haslinger has given the manuscript of my Variations to the Library. I think: "F[ools], as if you had nothing to keep".'

From a letter sent by Chopin do his family in Warsaw, Vienna 14 May 1831.

'The B♭ major Variations, of which I received a couple of days ago from Kassel, from a certain German enthused with these Variations, a ten-page review where, after a huge preface, he sets about dismantling them bar by bar – he explains that they are not variations like any other, but that it is some fantastical tableau. – Of the second Variation he says that Don Giovanni is running with Leporello, of the 3rd that he's hugging Zerlina, and Masetto in the left hand is angry – and of the 5th bar of the Adagio he states that Don Giovanni is kissing Zerlina in D♭ major. […] One could die from a German's imagination […]'

From a letter sent by Chopin to Tytus Woyciechowski in Poturzyn, Paris 12 December 1831.

'Hats off, gentlemen, a genius!'

Robert Schumann, 'Ein Werk II' [review of Chopin's Variations], *Allgemeine Musikalische Zeitung* 33 (1831).

o Wariacjach...

op. 2

„[...] mam do Ciebie interes następujący: Ponieważ teraz brzydka pogoda, rad bym napisać fortepian do Wariacji
na czysto. Do tego trzeba mi Twego egzemplarza, bądź więc łaskaw jutro mi go przynieś, a pojutrze
jedno i drugie dostaniesz."

Z listu F. Chopina do Jana Matuszyńskiego w Warszawie, Warszawa, zima 1827/1828.

„Myślę, że to Trio podobny los spotka, co moją Sonatę i Wariacje. Już są w Lipsku, pierwsza, jak wiesz
Elsnerowi przypisana, na drugich (może zbyt śmiały) twoje nakreśliłem imię. (Serce tak chciało,
przyjaźń nie wzbroniła, i Ty za złe nie bierz.)"

Z listu F. Chopina do Tytusa Woyciechowskiego w Poturzynie, Warszawa 9 IX 1828.

„[...] wczoraj więc, to jest we wtorek, wieczorem o godzinie 7-ej na teatrze cesarsko-królewskim opery na świat
wystąpiłem! [...] Skorom się na scenie pokazał, dostałem brawo; po odegraniu każdej wariacji takie były oklaski,
żem nie słyszał tutti orkiestry. Po skończeniu tyle klaskano, iż musiałem drugi raz wyjść i ukłonić się."

Z listu F. Chopina do rodziny w Warszawie, Wiedeń 12 VIII 1829.

„Musiałem na drugim koncercie grać też powtórnie Wariacje, bo się strasznie damom podobały i Haslingerowi.
Wyjdą w «Odeonie», spodziewam się, że dosyć honoru."

Z listu F. Chopina do Tytusa Woyciechowskiego w Poturzynie, Warszawa 12 IX 1829.

„Panna Belleville grała drukowane moje Wari[acje] w Wiedniu i jedną nawet umie na pamięć."

Z listu F. Chopina do Tytusa Woyciechowskiego w Poturzynie, Warszawa 5 VI 1830.

„Byłem też wczoraj z Kandlerem w cesarskiej bibliotece. [..] wystawcie sobie moje zdziwienie, gdy pomiędzy
nowszymi rękopisami widzę książkę w futerale z napisem Chopin. Coś to dosyć grubego w ładnej oprawie.
Myślę sobie, nigdym jeszcze o innym Chopinie nie słyszał [...] Wyjmuję, patrzę, moja ręka: a to Haslinger rękopism
moich Wariacji oddał do Biblioteki. Myślę sobie: «D[urnie], macie co chować»."

Z listu F. Chopina do rodziny w Warszawie, Wiedeń 14 V 1831.

„Wariacje B-dur, na które odebrałem przed paru dniami z Cassel od jednego Niemca, zaantuzjazmowanego [!]
tymi Wariacjami, dziesięcioarkuszową recenzję, gdzie po ogromnych przedmowach przystępuje do rozbioru onych
takt za taktem – tłomaczy, że to nie są wariacje jak każde inne, tylko że to jest jakieś fantastyczne tableau. –
Na drugą Wariację mówi, że Don Juan z Leporellem biega, na 3-cią, że ściska Zerlinkę, a Mazetto w lewej ręce
się gniewa – a na Adagia 5-ty takt powiada, że Don Juan całuje Zerlinkę w Des-dur. [...]
Umierać z imaginacji Niemca [...]"

Z listu F. Chopina do Tytusa Woyciechowskiego w Poturzynie, Paryż 12 XII 1831.

„Kapelusze z głów, Panowie, oto geniusz!"

Robert Schumann, *Ein Werk II* [recenzja *Wariacji* Chopina] , Allgemeine Musikalische Zeitung" 33 (1831).

ORCHESTRA

2 Flauti
2 Oboi
2 Clarinetti in si♭
2 Fagotti
2 Corni in fa
Timpani in si♭, fa
Violini I
Violini II
Viole
Violoncelli
Contrabassi

„La ci darem la mano" varié

A Mr Titus Woyciechowski

pour le Piano-forté avec accompagnement d'Orchestre

INTRODUZIONE

op. 2

11

14

16

THEMA

Var. II

* Inna wersja tego taktu – patrz *Komentarz źródłowy*.
  For another version of this bar, vide *Source Commentary*.

Var. III

* Inna wersja tego taktu – patrz *Komentarz źródłowy* do t. 175.
  For another version of this bar, vide *Source Commentary* to bar 175.

FWN 17 **A XVa**

Var. V

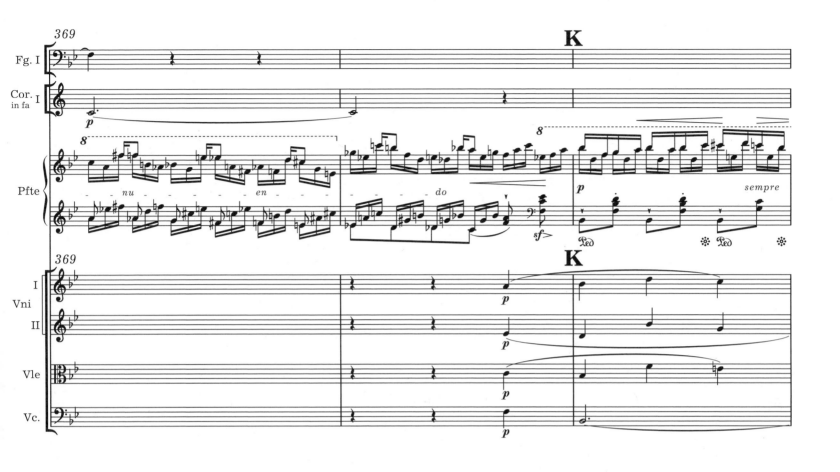

Okładka i opracowanie graficzne   ·   Cover design and graphics: MARIA EKIER
Tłumaczenie angielskie   ·   English translation: JOHN COMBER

Fundacja Wydania Narodowego Dzieł Fryderyka Chopina
ul. Okólnik 2, pok. 405, 00-368 Warszawa
www.chopin-nationaledition.com

Polskie Wydawnictwo Muzyczne SA
al. Krasińskiego 11a, Kraków
www.pwm.com.pl

Wyd. I. Printed in Poland 2020. Drukarnia REGIS Sp. z o.o.
05-230 Kobyłka, ul. Napoleona 4

ISMN 979-0-9013366-2-9

NATIONAL EDITION OF THE WORKS OF FRYDERYK CHOPIN

Plan of the edition

Series A. WORKS PUBLISHED DURING CHOPIN'S LIFETIME

Series B. WORKS PUBLISHED POSTHUMOUSLY

(The titles in square brackets [] have been reconstructed by the National Edition; the titles in slant marks // are still in use today but are definitely, or very probably, not authentic)

1 **A I** **Ballades** Opp. 23, 38, 47, 52

2 **A II** **Etudes** Opp. 10, 25, Three Etudes (Méthode des Méthodes)

3 **A III** **Impromptus** Opp. 29, 36, 51

4 **A IV** **Mazurkas (A)** Opp. 6, 7, 17, 24, 30, 33, 41, Mazurka in a (Gaillard), Mazurka in a (from the album La France Musicale /Notre Temps/), Opp. 50, 56, 59, 63

25 **B I** **Mazurkas (B)** in B♭, G, a, C, F, G, B♭, A♭, C, a, g, f

5 **A V** **Nocturnes** Opp. 9, 15, 27, 32, 37, 48, 55, 62

6 **A VI** **Polonaises (A)** Opp. 26, 40, 44, 53, 61

26 **B II** **Polonaises (B)** in B♭, g, A♭, g♯, d, f, b♭, B♭, G♭

7 **A VII** **Preludes** Opp. 28, 45

8 **A VIII** **Rondos** Opp. 1, 5, 16

9 **A IX** **Scherzos** Opp. 20, 31, 39, 54

10 **A X** **Sonatas** Opp. 35, 58

11 **A XI** **Waltzes (A)** Opp. 18, 34, 42, 64

27 **B III** **Waltzes (B)** in E, b, D♭, A♭, e, G♭, A♭, f, a

12 **A XII** **Various Works (A)** Variations brillantes Op. 12, Bolero, Tarantella, Allegro de concert, Fantaisie Op. 49, Berceuse, Barcarolle; *supplement* – Variation VI from "Hexameron"

28 **B IV** **Various Works (B)** Variations in E, Sonata in c (Op. 4)

29 **B V** **Various Compositions** Funeral March in c, [Variants] /Souvenir de Paganini/, Nocturne in e, Ecossaises in D, G, D♭, Contredanse, [Allegretto], Lento con gran espressione /Nocturne in c♯/, Cantabile in B♭, Presto con leggierezza /Prelude in A♭/, Impromptu in c♯ /Fantaisie-Impromptu/, "Spring" (version for piano), Sostenuto /Waltz in E♭/, Moderato /Feuille d'Album/, Galop Marquis, Nocturne in c

13 **A XIIIa** **Concerto in E minor** Op. 11 for piano and orchestra (version for one piano)

30 **B VIa** **Concerto in E minor** Op. 11 for piano and orchestra (version with second piano)

14 **A XIIIb** **Concerto in F minor** Op. 21 for piano and orchestra (version for one piano)

31 **B VIb** **Concerto in F minor** Op. 21 for piano and orchestra (version with second piano)

15 **A XIVa** **Concert Works** for piano and orchestra Opp. 2, 13, 14 (version for one piano)

32 **B VII** **Concert Works** for piano and orchestra Opp. 2, 13, 14, 22 (version with second piano)

16 **A XIVb** **Grande Polonaise in E♭ major** Op. 22 for piano and orchestra (version for one piano)

17 **A XVa** **Variations on "Là ci darem" from "Don Giovanni"** Op. 2. Score

18 **A XVb** **Concerto in E minor** Op. 11. Score (historical version)

33 **B VIIIa** **Concerto in E minor** Op. 11. Score (concert version)

19 **A XVc** **Fantasia on Polish Airs** Op. 13. Score

20 **A XVd** **Krakowiak** Op. 14. Score

21 **A XVe** **Concerto in F minor** Op. 21. Score (historical version)

34 **B VIIIb** **Concerto in F minor** Op. 21. Score (concert version)

22 **A XVf** **Grande Polonaise in E♭ major** Op. 22. Score

23 **A XVI** **Works for Piano and Cello** Polonaise Op. 3, Grand Duo Concertant, Sonata Op. 65

35 **B IX** **Rondo in C** for two pianos; **Variations in D** for four hands; *addendum* – working version of Rondo in C (for one piano)

24 **A XVII** **Piano Trio** Op. 8

36 **B X** **Songs**

37 **Supplement** Compositions partly by Chopin: Hexameron, Mazurkas in F♯, D, D, C, Variations for Flute and Piano; harmonizations of songs and dances: "The Dąbrowski Mazurka", "God who hast embraced Poland" (Largo) Bourrées in G, A, Allegretto in A-major/minor

WYDANIE NARODOWE DZIEŁ FRYDERYKA CHOPINA

Plan edycji

Seria A. UTWORY WYDANE ZA ŻYCIA CHOPINA

Seria B. UTWORY WYDANE POŚMIERTNIE

(Tytuły w nawiasach kwadratowych [] są tytułami zrekonstruowanymi przez WN, tytuły w nawiasach prostych // są dotychczas używanymi, z pewnością lub dużym prawdopodobieństwem, nieautentycznymi tytułami)

1 **A I**	**Ballady** op. 23, 38, 47, 52	
2 **A II**	**Etiudy** op. 10, 25, Trzy Etiudy (Méthode des Méthodes)	
3 **A III**	**Impromptus** op. 29, 36, 51	
4 **A IV**	**Mazurki (A)** op. 6, 7, 17, 24, 30, 33, 41, Mazurek a (Gaillard), Mazurek a (z albumu La France Musicale /Notre Temps/), op. 50, 56, 59, 63	25 **B I** **Mazurki (B)** B, G, a, C, F, G, B, As, C, a, g, f
5 **A V**	**Nokturny** op. 9, 15, 27, 32, 37, 48, 55, 62	
6 **A VI**	**Polonezy (A)** op. 26, 40, 44, 53, 61	26 **B II** **Polonezy (B)** B, g, As, gis, d, f, b, B, Ges
7 **A VII**	**Preludia** op. 28, 45	
8 **A VIII**	**Ronda** op. 1, 5, 16	
9 **A IX**	**Scherza** op. 20, 31, 39, 54	
10 **A X**	**Sonaty** op. 35, 58	
11 **A XI**	**Walce (A)** op. 18, 34, 42, 64	27 **B III** **Walce (B)** E, h, Des, As, e, Ges, As, f, a
12 **A XII**	**Dzieła różne (A)** Variations brillantes op. 12, Bolero, Tarantela, Allegro de concert, Fantazja op. 49, Berceuse, Barkarola; *suplement* – Wariacja VI z „Hexameronu"	28 **B IV** **Dzieła różne (B)** Wariacje E, Sonata c (op. 4)
		29 **B V** **Różne utwory** Marsz żałobny c, [Warianty] /Souvenir de Paganini/, Nokturn e, Ecossaises D, G, Des, Kontredans, [Allegretto], Lento con gran espressione /Nokturn cis/, Cantabile B, Presto con leggierezza /Preludium As/, Impromptu cis /Fantaisie-Impromptu/, „Wiosna" (wersja na fortepian), Sostenuto /Walc Es/, Moderato /Kartka z albumu/, Galop Marquis, Nokturn c
13 **A XIIIa**	**Koncert e-moll** op. 11 na fortepian i orkiestrę (wersja na jeden fortepian)	30 **B VIa** **Koncert e-moll** op. 11 na fortepian i orkiestrę (wersja z drugim fortepianem)
14 **A XIIIb**	**Koncert f-moll** op. 21 na fortepian i orkiestrę (wersja na jeden fortepian)	31 **B VIb** **Koncert f-moll** op. 21 na fortepian i orkiestrę (wersja z drugim fortepianem)
15 **A XIVa**	**Utwory koncertowe** na fortepian i orkiestrę op. 2, 13, 14 (wersja na jeden fortepian)	32 **B VII** **Utwory koncertowe** na fortepian i orkiestrę op. 2, 13, 14, 22 (wersja z drugim fortepianem)
16 **A XIVb**	**Polonez Es-dur** op. 22 na fortepian i orkiestrę (wersja na jeden fortepian)	
17 **A XVa**	**Wariacje na temat z** *Don Giovanniego* **Mozarta** op. 2. Partytura	
18 **A XVb**	**Koncert e-moll** op. 11. Partytura (wersja historyczna)	33 **B VIIIa** **Koncert e-moll** op. 11. Partytura (wersja koncertowa)
19 **A XVc**	**Fantazja na tematy polskie** op. 13. Partytura	
20 **A XVd**	**Krakowiak** op. 14. Partytura	
21 **A XVe**	**Koncert f-moll** op. 21. Partytura (wersja historyczna)	34 **B VIIIb** **Koncert f-moll** op. 21. Partytura (wersja koncertowa)
22 **A XVf**	**Polonez Es-dur** op. 22. Partytura	
23 **A XVI**	**Utwory na fortepian i wiolonczelę** Polonez op. 3, Grand Duo Concertant, Sonata op. 65	35 **B IX** **Rondo C-dur** na dwa fortepiany; **Wariacje D-dur** na 4 ręce; *dodatek* – wersja robocza Ronda C-dur (na jeden fortepian)
24 **A XVII**	**Trio na fortepian, skrzypce i wiolonczelę** op. 8	36 **B X** **Pieśni i piosnki**

37 **Suplement** Utwory częściowego autorstwa Chopina: Hexameron, Mazurki Fis, D, D, C, Wariacje na flet i fortepian; harmonizacje pieśni i tańców: „Mazurek Dąbrowskiego", „Boże, coś Polskę" (Largo), Bourrées G, A, Allegretto A-dur/a-moll

FRYDERYK CHOPIN
VARIATIONS Op. 2
score

Source Commentary (abridged)
Performance Commentary

SOURCE COMMENTARY /ABRIDGED/

Initial remarks

The present commentary concerns only the orchestra part (the solo part is discussed in the commentaries to the *Variations* in the versions for one piano and with second piano). It sets out the principles behind the editing of the musical text and discusses the more important discrepancies between sources; in addition, it signals the most crucial alterations made in the printed scores of the *Variations* (none of which was published during Chopin's lifetime).

A precise characterisation of all the sources, their relations to one another, a detailed presentation of the differences appearing between them, and also reproductions of characteristic fragments of the different sources are all contained in a separately published *Source Commentary*.

The sign → indicates a relationship between sources, and should be read as 'and the source(s) based thereon'.

Chopin's scores

Editing the scores of Chopin's works with orchestra (and also the *Trio*, Op. 8), one encounters certain specific problems. In keeping with the frequent practice of that period, only the separate parts of particular instruments were published. Aware of this situation, Chopin probably contented himself with scores of a partly working character, only writing any final touches (including more exact performance markings) into the separate parts. It is almost certain that he entrusted both the preparing of the parts and at least some of the routine supplementing of such things as performance markings to friends with some experience in such work ('Nidecki [...] has looked through with and corrected the orchestral parts'*) or to professional copyists – a practice which can easily lead to numerous inaccuracies and inconsistencies, as well as serious errors, not always easy to identify.

Variations in B flat major, Op. 2

Sources

AsI Working autograph of the score (The Morgan Pierpont Library, New York), inscribed 'Variations sur le Theme de Mozart FFCh 1827'. The notation is hurried, at times abbreviated, with numerous corrections made probably at different times (the manuscript also contains the note 'went to Vienna in 1829'). Neither the piano part nor the orchestra part has a final, polished form, and in later sources they were both considerably altered and supplemented. Performance markings appear in **AsI** only sporadically. It is particularly difficult to read the parts of the Vc. & Cb., written on a single stave; although Chopin certainly wished to differentiate their parts (e.g. through the use in certain places of cellos only), he marked this in an inconsistent and imprecise way.

It is difficult to state whether there existed some later manuscript of the score of the *Variations*. Although this cannot be excluded, one can imagine both the work's performance with Chopin as soloist and also the preparation of the orchestral material for print on the basis of the parts prepared from **AsI** and then corrected and copied out.

[P] Lost manuscript parts, serving as the base text for the German first edition, notated according to the corrected and supplemented parts prepared on the basis of **AsI** or of a lost later manuscript of the score. Compared to **AsI** the version of **[P]** displays on one hand changes and clarifications undoubtedly given by Chopin, e.g.
— removal of trumpets;
— differentiation of articulation of Vc. & Cb. in bars 322 ff;
— changes of rhythm on the 2nd quaver of bars 96 & 98 and 200, 202 & 206.

---

* From a letter sent by Chopin to his family, Vienna, 12 August 1829; he was referring to the *Variations in B♭*, Op. 2 and/or the *Krakowiak*, Op. 14.

On the other hand, there are also more or less probable errors and misunderstandings, e.g.
— the probably mistaken use of Cb. in bars 6-8 and 370-372;
— the Vc. in bars 331-334 not marked pizz.
We encounter a similar situation in the *Krakowiak*, Op. 14 (see commentary to score).

A Autograph fair copy of the version for one piano (Österreichische Nationalbibliothek, Vienna), serving as the base text for the German first edition. The notation is most meticulous, with very few deletions and corrections; it displays an impressive array of precise performance markings. Despite this, it contains several unquestionable errors and a great many inaccuracies in the notation of accidentals.

GE First German edition of the version for one piano, Tobias Haslinger (T.H.5489.), Vienna, April 1830. This was prepared from **A**, with the text generally reproduced very carefully and the necessary corrections made to accidentals. In spite of this, an overly mechanical reading of the manuscript led to slurs, dynamic markings and *staccato* signs being situated inaccurately or erroneously in many places. It seems unlikely that Chopin proofread this edition, although his hand cannot be precluded here and there.
There exists a later impression of **GE**, in which a number of most probably arbitrary changes were made (e.g. fingering added in several places). Copies of the two impressions display different details on the cover.
In December 1839 the same firm published a second edition of the *Variations* (T.H.7714.), with further arbitrary changes.

GEP Orchestral parts appended to **GE** (same firm and number), based on **[P]**. It is unlikely that Chopin helped to prepare them.

FE First French edition of the version for one piano, M. Schlesinger (M.S.1312), Paris, beginning of 1833, based on the first impression of **GE** and proofread by Chopin. Later impressions (from 1845) – with the original plate number retained – were signed by Schlesinger's successor, G. Brandus.

FEP Orchestral parts appended to **FE** (same firm and number), based on **GEP** and proofread most probably with the participation or according to the suggestions of Chopin (e.g. in bars 14, 227, 240-243). **FEP** contains a number of errors and inaccuracies.

EE First English edition, Wessel & C° (W & C°. N°. 820; on two pages 821), London, spring 1833. Presents a revised text of **GE**; Chopin did not participate in its preparation.
The NE editors were unable to find orchestral parts prepared by Wessel & C°, and so it may be assumed that – as with other Chopin works with orchestra – the orchestral material was not printed by the English publisher.

SBH First edition of the score as part of an edition of the complete works of Chopin (*Erste kritisch durchgesehene Gesamtausgabe*), Breitkopf & Härtel (C XII 1), Leipzig 1880. Numerous revisions setting dynamic and articulation markings in order were made here, as well as several other, arbitrary, changes. Only the most important of these are noted in the further part of this commentary.

SSi Edition of the score of the *Variations* prepared by K. Sikorski as part of an edition of the complete works of Chopin, Instytut Fryderyka Chopina & Polskie Wydawnictwo Muzyczne (PWM-3732), Warsaw-Kraków 1961. This was based on **SBH**, with a number of arbitrary changes made.

Editorial principles for the orchestra part
As the basic text, we adopt **GEP**, compared with **AsI** to eliminate likely errors. We take account of changes in **FEP** that may be Chopin's, as well as the version for one piano, which he meticulously polished, particularly his own reductions of the orchestra part; this version is considered on the basis of **A** with later Chopin changes in **FE**.
We set in order the very numerous inconsistencies and inaccuracies in the notation of articulation and dynamic markings, endeavouring, by means of the fewest possible interventions, to obtain a notation which conveys the musical sense in the most legible way.
We transpose the parts of the B♭ basso horns that appear in the original score to the pitch of F, most commonly used today.

The piano part comes from volume 32 **B VII** (version with second piano). Omitted here are the fingering and elements of notation provided by the editors which have no effect on the acoustic relations between the solo and orchestra parts (brackets, minor variants).

Introduzione

p. 11 *Bar 1* Vc. **FEP** give here f, which is certainly an error.

Bars 5-8 Vni, Vle. We give the dynamic markings of **GEP** (→**FEP**), checked and supplemented on the basis of **A**.

Bars 6-8 Cb. In **GEP** (→**FEP**) the double basses double the part of the cellos from the **A** in bar 6. We give the version of **AsI**, precisely notated in this respect and confirmed by the correction to the version for one piano which Chopin made in **FE** (change of 2nd, 3rd and 4th crotchets of bar 8 from F to F_1-F).

p. 12 *Bar 14* Vc. & Cb. As the last note **GEP** have G. The error was corrected in **FEP**.

p. 13 *Bar 36* Fl. I. On the 4th beat we give the dotted rhythm written in **AsI**. **GEP** (→**FEP**) have even quavers, most probably by mistake (cf. Pfte & Vni I).

p. 14 *Bar 40* Vni I, Vc. & Cb. **GEP** (→**FEP**) give here p. The virtuosic chordal texture and f dynamic of the solo part suggest an error, which is confirmed by the f appearing in the Vni II & Vle parts.

p. 17 *Bar 60* Fl. I. Neither **AsI** nor **GEP** (→**FEP**) have ♮ before the e^2 on the 4th beat.

Thema

p. 19 *Bars 96-97* Vni, Vle. The dynamic markings that appear in **GEP** (→**FEP**) are certainly imprecise or erroneous (the scope and direction of the hairpins and the ff in Vni, Vc & Cb.). We leave only those which do not contradict the markings written by Chopin in the autograph of the version for one piano (**A**).

Bars 96, 98 & analog. Fl., Ob., Cl., Fg., Vni, Vle, Vc. & Cb. On the basis of **GEP** (→**FEP**) it is difficult to establish which rhythms – ♫ or ♪.♪ – Chopin intended for the 2nd quaver in the 1st and 3rd bars of the *Tutti* ending the theme and the first 4 variations (in the theme and Var. IV also in the 5th bar). Only in Vars. II & IV do all the parts have the same rhythm: ♫. In the others, both rhythms appear:
Theme – ♪.♪ in Vni I, Vle, Vc. & Cb. in both bars and in Vni II & Fl. in the 1st bar (bar 96); ♫ in the other parts;
Var. I – ♪.♪ in Vc. & Cb. (in both bars); ♫ in the other parts;
Var. III – ♪.♪ in Vni & Vle (in both bars); ♫ in the other parts.
Reference to the autographs also fails to provide evidence for straightforward conclusions to be drawn:

— in **AsI** the orchestral parts have only the rhythm ♫, but in the piano part (also including Chopin's reductions of *Tutti* passages) the rhythm ♪.♪ appears in the 1st bar of the theme and Var. IV;

— in **A** the reductions of the *Tutti* passages have the rhythm ♪.♪ in the 1st bar of the theme and in all the bars in question of Vars. III & IV.
The simultaneous occurrence of different rhythms in the parts of different instruments is not musically justified in these places and probably arose from changes made by Chopin and inaccuracies and errors made when writing out and correcting the parts. The reconstruction proposed below, which the editors consider satisfactory, accounts for the state that exists in the sources:

— originally (**AsI**) all these places had the uniform rhythm ♫;

— in the *Tutti* ending the theme and the slower variations (III and originally IV), Chopin decided to introduce the rhythm ♪.♪; this stage was conserved in the notation of **A**;

— taking account of the quick tempo of the final version of Var. IV, in [**P**] Chopin introduced the rhythm ♪.♪ only in the theme and Var. III; for some reason (haste on Chopin's part? inattention on the copyist's?) the changes were not applied to all the parts and places (it seems crucial, however, that they were made without error in the basic melodic part, namely Vni I);

— the rhythm ♪.♪ in Vc. & Cb. in Var. I is the result either of a copying error (an identical – except for the rhythm – fragment of the theme was written; this hypothesis is strengthened by the erroneous dynamic marking, cf. comments to bars 96-97 and 128) or of a misunderstanding during the implementation of the corrections described above (the change of rhythm was introduced in this part in Var. I instead of Var. III).

Bars 96, 102, 107, 175 & analog. Timp. In **AsI** Chopin erroneously wrote the demisemiquaver tremolo that fills the beamless quaver as ♪. In **GEP** (→**FEP**) the missing flag was added, but 3 strokes were left in the tremolo sign, as a result of which – certainly contrary to Chopin's intentions – the notated speed of the tremolo was doubled.

Bars 99, 171 & 203 Fl. II & Vni II. In **GEP** (→**FEP**) in bar 99 the Fl. II doubles the Fl. I part, and in bars 171 & 203 c^2 is missing on the 1st quaver in the Vni II part. Analysis of **AsI** shows that Chopin did not intend any pitch differences in the 1st four-bar segment of these *Tutti*.

Bar 102 Cb. As the 4th quaver **GEP** (→**FEP**) have F. This is most probably an error, echoing the ambiguous notation of **AsI** (the Cb. entrance in this bar was written at concert pitch, with the octave transposition overlooked). In **AsI** Chopin wrote the Cb. entrance in bar 134 similarly – as F; there, however, **GEP** (→**FEP**) correctly have f.

Bar 103 Vle. As the 3rd quaver **GEP** erroneously have d^1.

Bars 103, 135, 175 & 207 Vni I. The notes d^2 on the 2nd quaver (in bars 175 & 207 also on the 3rd) were added during the proofreading of **GEP**. The fourfold repetition of this change in similar, albeit not identical, places precludes the possibility of error; furthermore, it is hard to imagine that additions of this kind could have been made without Chopin's knowledge.

Var. I

p. 20 *Bars 108 & 124* Vle. We give the version of **GEP** (→**FEP**), although the difference between these bars may be accidental (**AsI** has d^1 in both bars).

Bar 110 Vle. The sources give here f, yet in the analogous bar 126 they have a. In the editors' opinion, the version of bar 110 is probably a mistake, made during the correcting of **AsI**: the top voices of the accompaniment in bars 109-110, the minims g-c^1 and a-c^1-eb^1, were originally given to the violins alone; Chopin subsequently divided them among three parts (as it was written without corrections in bar 126), but copied f when transferring a in bar 110 from Vni II to Vle.

p. 22 *Bar 128* Vc. & Cb. **GEP** (→**FEP**) have here, most probably by mistake, ff.

Var. II

p. 24 *Bar 150* Vle. As the 3rd quaver **GEP** erroneously have a.

p. 26 *Bars 171-172* Cl I. Missing in **SBH** is the tie sustaining g^2.

Bar 172 Vni & Vle. We give the rhythm of **As**I (written there as ♩ ♪♪), concordant with the rhythm appearing both in Vc. & Cb. and also in Chopin's reduction of this passage in **A**. **GEP** (→**FEP**) have here ♩ ♪♪ (without ties).

Bar 173 Fl I. Chopin added the mordent in the version for one piano while proofreading **FE**. It also appears in the Fl part of **As**I, but is absent from both **A** and **GEP** (→**FEP**). Chopin either mistakenly omitted the sign in a certain group of sources or else returned to his original idea after a period of vacillation.

Bar 174 Vle. We give the ⎯⎯ introduced during the proofreading of **FEP** instead of the ⎯⎯ that appears in **GEP**.
Cl. I & Fg. II. In **GEP** (→**FEP**) the entrance on the 4th quaver is marked with the sign *f*. This is certainly an imprecise notation, and so we give markings which accord with the other parts and with Chopin's reduction of this passage in **A**.

Bars 175 & 207 Fl., Ob., Cl., Vni & Vle. Both in **As**I and in **GEP** & **FEP** (our text) the 3rd quaver is a repeat of the 2nd. This is also the original version in Chopin's piano reduction of these bars, written in **As**I and – with minor alterations – in **A**. However, during the proofreading of **FE** Chopin changed the sound of this quaver, replacing the B♭ major chord with a single note *bb*. It would be natural to regard this change as applying to the orchestral version as well (cf. comments to bars 173 & 260, and also to the *Concerto in F minor*, Op. 21, movt. III, bars 19 & 343). In this case, however, we are dealing with a correction – most probably Chopin's – of **FEP** in the Vni I part (cf. comment to bars 103, 135, 175 & 207), which should be seen as manifesting the composer's acceptance of the chordal version of this quaver. In this situation, it is difficult to conclude whether in this group of instruments Chopin wanted on the last quaver of Vars. II & III to leave the full B♭ major chord or – in line with the way in which he revised **FE** – only *bb*. We give the former possibility in the main text and the proposed execution of the latter below (in the orchestral materials this version is given as a variant):

Var. III

p. 28

Bars 199 & 239 Vni I. We write out the termination of the trill which opens the *Tutti* after the fashion of bars 95, 127 & 167.

Bar 206 Tutti. The rhythm ♪.♪ on the 2nd quaver of the bar appears in **GEP** (→**FEP**) only in the Vni I part; the other parts have ♪♪. Even semiquavers appear in this place also in **As**I, both in the orchestral parts and in the piano. This means that the dotted rhythm was introduced by Chopin later and was most probably meant to concern all the parts (cf. comment to bars 96, 98 & analog.). This is confirmed in the version of **A**, in which Chopin's piano reduction of this passage has the following form:

Var. IV

In **As**I this variation is written in an earlier version, in the solo part based on a different textural idea:

Chopin most probably made the change just before submitting the work to his publisher, since **A**, on which the print was based, contains the variation in two versions: the crossed-through original version and the final version added at the end of the manuscript. However, the harmonic structure of the original version is almost identical to the structure of the final version, and so the orchestral accompaniment remained practically unaltered (strictly speaking, the minor changes which in this variation appear between **As**I and **GEP** were most probably introduced by Chopin before he altered the texture of the solo part). In this situation, one may wonder whether the composer closely checked that the new solo part was concordant with the old accompaniment. In the editors' opinion, the following elements of the orchestra part need to be deliberated:
— the bass voice, which corresponds note for note with the original solo part but displays discrepancies (in bars 210 & analog., 223 and 226) in relation to its final version;
— the omission in the printed version of the entrance of the Fg. & Cl. in bars 215-216;
— the uniform dynamics, taking no account of the distinct contrasts in bars 216, 224, 228, 232 & 236 of the solo part;
— the chord on the last quaver of bar 227.
The solutions adopted are discussed below in the comments to particular bars.

Bars 209 & 217 Vni II. At the beginning of the bar **GEP** (→**FEP**) erroneously have c^1 (the error is written only once, since bars 216-222 are marked as a repeat of bars 208-214). **As**I has the correct text.

Bars 210 & analog., 223 and 226 Vc. & Cb. As already mentioned at the start of the commentary to this variation, the line of the bottom notes of the LH in the solo piano part does not tally in these bars with the bass line played by the Vc. & Cb. However, this does not give rise to harmonic disagreement, and in bars 210 & analog. and 226 it even enhances the relations between the solo part and the accompaniment. For this reason, we leave the version of **GEP** (→**FEP**) with no changes.

p. 29 *Bars 215-216* Cl. & Fg. **As**I has here the following motif, which is a repeat of the corresponding fragment of the theme:

This entrance was subsequently omitted, since at the stage of writing **A** Chopin relinquished the repetition of the 1st 8-bar unit of the original version of Var. IV (see note at the start of the commentary to this variation). After changing the texture of the solo part, Chopin restored the repeat of the opening 8-bar segment, yet the motif in question does not appear in **GEP** (→**FEP**). It is difficult today to affirm with the utmost certainty whether this was a conscious decision on the part of the composer or rather oversight. However, given that, in restoring the repeat, Chopin must have made changes to the orchestra part in these bars (in the version without repeat bar 215 was not notated), we consider it more likely that he deliberately omitted the motif; consequently, we leave the printed version without the additions.

Bars 216, 228, 232 & 236 Vni, Vle, Vc. & Cb. We alter or supplement the dynamic signs, matching the dynamics of the orchestral accompaniment to the dynamically contrastive final version of the solo part (see note at the start of this variation). **GEP** (→**FEP**) have *p*, in bars 216 & 232 and no markings in bars 228 & 236.

p. 30 *Bar 227* Vni II, Vle. On the 2nd beat **As**I has 2 quavers in both parts: c^1-*b* in Vni II; *a*-*g#* in Vle. The change of chord on the last quaver corresponds there to the harmony of the solo part (in **As**I Var. IV is written in the original version, later completely changed by Chopin – see above). In **GEP** the orchestra part remained unaltered, but this makes the 4th quaver harmonically at odds with the final version of the piano part, in which the whole 2nd half of the bar is based on an F major chord. The following facts attest that this was not an effect intended by Chopin:
— the strictly accompanying character of the orchestra part, which plays solely chordal notes of the harmonic ground (discounting a few solos in the *Introduction* and in the closing segment of the final *Alla Polacca*);
— the partial removal of this disagreement during the proofreading of **FEP** (the quavers *a*-*g#* of the violas were replaced by a crotchet *a*).
In the main text we complete this fragmentary – in our opinion – correction, analogously removing *b* on the 4th quaver in the Vni II. As a variant, we give the latest source version: that of **FEP**.

Bar 235 Fl. I. In **FEP** the Fl. II part was mistakenly printed here.

p. 31 *Bars 240-245* We give the *cresc.* which during the proofreading of **FEP** replaced the *rinforz.* that appears in **GEP** (both terms appear in particular parts in different bars, from 240 to 244). The change may have been inspired by Chopin.

Bars 246-247 Fg. In **GEP** (→**FEP**) the parts of the two bassoons are switched, which is most probably a mistake. Although **As**I does have a slightly different version here, the difference would appear to concern the rhythm only; in respect to the relations between the two instruments, no details of the notation suggest that the lower part was to be played by the Fg. I.

Bars 247, 249 & 251 Vc., Cb. The rhythms ♩♪ that appear in these bars in Chopin's piano reduction in **A** bid us ponder the rhythm of the orchestral bass parts. However, the corrections visible in **As**I prove that Chopin began with even semiquavers and eventually returned to them, only temporarily considering the introduction of dotted rhythms. See comment to bars 96, 98 & analog.

Bars 253-254 Vle. **GEP** (→**FEP**) have here minims *gb* and *f*, as in the Fg. I part. In the editors' opinion, this is probably a remnant of the original version, in which the parts of the Fg. I & Vle (as written by us here) were switched. This version – with a tied minim *eb* in the Fg. I part and a motif *gb*-*f* in the Vle – was originally noted in **As**I. Chopin subsequently altered the Fg. I part, removing *eb* and adding *gb*-*f*, which gave in bar 254 a perfect F major chord, without the seventh *eb*. However, both the piano reductions of these bars written in Chopin's hand (in **As**I & **A**) contain the note *eb* in bar 254 as well, and so one can hardly assume that Chopin did indeed wish to remove it from the orchestra part. For this reason, we consider it more likely that the corrections visible in **As**I constitute only half of the intended alterations, which were to have been completed by the addition of a held *eb* in the Vle part.

Vc. & Cb. **As**I has [music notation] here, simplified in **GEP** (→**FEP**) – possibly by mistake – to [music notation] (in both parts). In Chopin's piano reduction in **As**I the bass note in bar 254 is *F*, subsequently altered in **A** to the octave F-F_1. We give a version modelled on **As**I and also taking account of the lowering of the bass introduced by Chopin in **A**.

Var. V

p. 32 *Bar 255* Timp. We give the two versions of the beginning of the *Adagio* in accordance with **GEP** (→**FEP**), in which the repeat of bars 255-262 is in the Timp. part entirely written out in notes. In **SBH** this differentiation was overlooked.

Bar 260 Vc. & Cb. We give the crotchets *db*-*c* on the basis of the revision of **FE**, in which the octaves *Db*-*db* and *C*-*c* were added in smaller notes, used in the version for one piano for notating the reduction of the orchestra part. The addition was certainly made by Chopin, who undoubtedly intended it to concern also the full orchestral version of the work. Although Chopin did not indicate which instruments he had in mind, in this context it could only have been Vc. & Cb.

p. 33 *Bar 263* Vni I, Vc. & Cb. **GEP** (→**FEP**) have here *p*. On account of the piano's *ppp* we give in all the string parts the *pp* that appears in Vle.

Bars 268-270 The dynamic markings of **GEP** (→**FEP**) seem imprecise and incomplete here: the *pp* in the Vle part appears already in bar 268, and in the bass voice it is entirely absent. We modify and supplement the signs, taking into account the undoubtedly more precise markings of the solo piano.

Alla polacca

p. 34 *Bars 273-282* Vc. & Cb. In **GEP** (→**FEP**) the double basses double the Vc. part. From bar 275, where the piano comes in, this is at odds with the *cello* clearly marked in **As**I. It seems, however, that Chopin also intended the previous two-bar phrase, which in bar 273 exceeds the normal range of the double bass, to be played only by the cellos (and bassoons).

Bar 274 Timp. We give the version of **As**I, unambiguous when checked more precisely. However, the notation of this bar may have been misread by the copyist, since Chopin, after notating bars 271-274 in the actual sound, *B*(*Bb*)-*F*, wished to change the notation to the conventional *c*-*G* and so scratched out the old note heads. But he wrote the new heads only in bars 271-272. In the case of the minim in bar 274 this made it more difficult to read the rhythm and may have brought about the probably erroneous version of **GEP** (→**FEP**): [music notation].

p. 35   *Bar 284* Ob. I. We give the grace note at the beginning of the bar in accordance with **As**I. Its absence from **GEP** (→**FEP**) is probably the result of inattention during copying.

p. 36   *Bars 287-288* Vc. & Cb. We give the version of **GEP** (→**FEP**). The 'splitting' of the bass line on the last quaver of bar 287 and the 2nd quaver of bar 288 was intended by Chopin all along, as is attested by the notation of **As**I:

In **SBH** the two parts were unified in accordance with the Vc. part.

Bar 289 Fg. II. In **GEP** (→**FEP**) the first 2 quavers are written an octave higher (in unison with Fg. I), which is probably a mistake. We give the text of **As**I.
Vni II & Vle. On the 2nd beat in **SBH** the bottom notes of the Vni II part were arbitrarily moved to the Vle part.

Bar 290 Fl. & Vle. The hairpins ⸺ and accents were added – probably by Chopin – during the proofreading of **FEP**.

Bars 291-305 Vc. & Cb. In **GEP** (→**FEP**) the double basses double the Vc. part from bar 293 to the beginning of bar 304. In the editors' opinion, this is one of several misunderstandings in this area. Although it was admittedly not marked in this segment in **As**I, we do find indications of the use of cellos alone in other passages with a similar texture and character (bars 275-282 & 309-311). Reinforcing the accompaniment would merely make it difficult for the soloist to present all the nuances of the elegant solo part, with its self-sufficient sound.

p. 38   *Bars 309-311* Vc. & Cb. Not marked in **GEP** (→**FEP**) is the use of cellos alone, contrary to Chopin's clear indication in **As**I.

p. 41   *Bars 331-334* Vc. Omitted in **GEP** (→**FEP**) is the indication pizz. that appears in **As**I.

p. 42   *Bar 337* Fg. II. As the 2nd note **GEP** (→**FEP**) has *f*, certainly by mistake; also most probably erroneous is the rhythm of the 1st beat (even quavers). We give the undoubted version of **As**I.

Bar 340 Vni & Vle. Repeated here in **GEP** (→**FEP**) is *f*, We give the hairpins ⸺ written in **As**I.

p. 45   *Bar 359* Vni. We give the text of **As**I. Omitted in **GEP** (→**FEP**) – most probably by mistake – is the quaver *bb* in the Vni II part. Additionally, in **SBH** the quaver *d¹* in the Vni I was removed.
Vc. & Cb. In **As**I Chopin clearly indicated that from the 2nd quaver the cellos play alone. In **GEP** (→**FEP**) this differentiation of the two parts was ignored.

p. 47   *Bars 370-372* Cb. In **GEP** (→**FEP**) the double basses double here the Vc. part, contrary to the clear markings of **As**I.

p. 48   *Bars 375-376* Vc. We give the *Eb-F* on the 2nd and 3rd crotchets in accordance with **As**I. Most probably by mistake, **GEP** (→**FEP**) have here *eb-f*.

Bar 379 Ob. I & Cl. II. In **GEP** (→**FEP**) these instruments double – most probably erroneously – the minim of the Cl. I. We give the version of **As**I.

Bar 380 Timp. **GEP** (→**FEP**) have only 2 strokes in the tremolo sign, probably by mistake. We give the demisemiquavers notated in **As**I, more natural in this context.

Jan Ekier
Paweł Kamiński

6

PERFORMANCE COMMENTARY

The orchestral parts may be borrowed from the Biblioteka Materiałów Orkiestrowych PWM, ul. Fredry 8, 00-097 Warszawa, tel. +48 22-635-3550, fax +48 22-826-9780, www.pwm.com.pl, e-mail: bmo@pwm.com.pl

Remarks on the musical text

Editorial additions are given in square brackets [].

Long accent signs signify accents of a primarily expressive character, in which the accented part generally lasts slightly longer than with a normal accent (with shorter rhythmic values, it sometimes covers two or three notes) and the fall in the intensity of the sound is smoother.

General problems of the interpretation of Chopin's works will be discussed in a separate volume entitled *Introduction to the National Edition*, in the section entitled 'Issues relating to performance'.

Variations in B flat major, Op. 2

The tempos of the *Tutti* after the theme and first 4 variations may raise doubts. The lack of new tempo markings suggests the maintaining on each occasion of a tempo concordant with the authentic metronome marking given at the start of the theme or given variation. In this way, however, these segments – in spite of their almost identical texture – would be played at three distinctly different tempos ($\downarrow$=58-63 after the theme and Var. III, $\downarrow$=76 after Var. I, $\downarrow$=92 after Vars. II and IV). In the editors' opinion, it is possible that Chopin intended the metronome tempos to refer only to the texturally differentiated passages with the participation of the solo piano, with the orchestral interpolations retaining a uniform tempo, emphasising their ritornello character. Taking this into account, three groups of solutions may be proposed:

— performing each *Tutti* at the tempo of the theme or variation that precedes it, with the character of particular entries differentiated;

— performing all the *Tutti* at the same tempo, whilst conserving the most uniform character possible; this could be a tempo from the range $\downarrow$=58-76 (between the tempo of the theme and the tempo of Var. I), e.g. $\downarrow$=66-69;

— a 'mixed' performance, e.g. the *Tutti* after the theme with no tempo change ($\downarrow$=58) and the rest at the tempo of Var. I ($\downarrow$=76), or the *Tutti* after the theme and Var. III with no tempo change ($\downarrow$=58/63) and the rest at the tempo of Var. I ($\downarrow$=76).

Jan Ekier,
Paweł Kamiński